## Amazing Verse

Edited By Bobby Tobolik

First published in Great Britain in 2020 by:

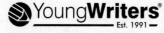

Young Writers
Remus House
Coltsfoot Drive
Peterborough
PE2 9BF
Telephone: 01733 890066
Website: www.youngwriters.co.uk

Printed and bound in the UK by BookPrintingUK
Website: www.bookprintinguk.com
YB0448U

Dear Reader,

Welcome to a fun-filled book of acrostic poems!

Here at Young Writers, we are delighted to introduce our new poetry competition for KS1 pupils, *My First Acrostic: Animal Adventures*. Acrostic poems are an enjoyable way to introduce pupils to the world of poetry and allow the young writer to open their imagination to a range of topics of their choice. The colourful and engaging entry forms allowed even the youngest (or most reluctant) of pupils to create a poem using the acrostic technique and with that, encouraged them to include other literary techniques such as similes and description. Here at Young Writers we are passionate about introducing the love and art of creative writing to the next generation and we love being a part of their journey.

From the jungle to the ocean, pets to mythical monsters, these pupils take you on a journey through the animal kingdom and showcase their budding creativity along the way. So we invite you to dive into these pages and take a glimpse into these blossoming young writers' minds. We hope you will relish these roarsome poems as much as we have.

# Contents

Jade Storey (7)     59

## Enborne CE Primary School, Enborne

Lyla Wisbey (7)     60
Harry Pearce (6)     61
Nina Powell (6)     62
Gracie Keel (6)     63
Harvey Burton (7)     64
Oliver Withers (8)     65
Tamilore Ganiyu (7)     66
Georgina Murray (5)     67
Freddie Ashbrook (8)     68
Ethan Hawkett (6)     69

## Hindhayes Infant School, Street

Melek Ozsevgec (6)     70
Bo Birkett (6)     71
Archie Duffy (6)     72
Tamzin Austwick (5)     73
Emily Buxton (6)     74
Leo Carombayenin (5)     75
Jack Molland (6)     76

## Holy Cross & All Saints RC Primary School, Eccles

Ava Sinclair (6)     77
Dillon Dwyer (6)     78
Felix Krzykwa (6)     79
Kevin Mathew (6), William     80
Vennard (5) & Daniel Jackson (6)
Basit Dauda (6)     81
Evelyn Nel (5)     82
Finley Winter (6)     83
Ethan Milton (6)     84
Harry McGill (6)     85
Joshua Hallworth (6)     86
Joshua Pollock (6) & Sam     87
Oscar Pennington (6)     88

## Kessingland CE Primary Academy, Kessingland

Marcus Pope-Brannon (7)     89
Henry Daws (7)     90
Fred Capps-Smith (6)     91
Niamh Weatherington (6)     92
Buddy Byron-Weatherill (6)     93
Imogen Loud (7)     94

## Magna Carta Primary Academy, Stansted Mountfitchet

Alfie Smith (6)     95

## Old Buckenham Hall School, Ipswich

Roseanna Sloper (7)     96
Rufus Wells (7)     97
Samuel Gosling (7)     98
Thomas Gillman (7)     99
Sophie Keaney (7)     100
Lauren Hewitt (7)     101
Giles Roberts (6)     102
Charlotte Warner (7)     103
Flora Surguy (5)     104
Amelia Mason-Sinclair (7)     105
Daisy Templer (6)     106
Rosie Clark (7)     107
Rory Ramsay (6)     108
Nixon Johnson (7)     109
Llywelyn Griffiths (6)     110

## St John's Priory School, Banbury

Arthur Price (6)     111
Arthur Price (6)     112
Atia D     113
Jayden T (6)     114
Charlotte A (6)     115
Ash L     116
Beatrix M (6)     117
Xavier R     118
Leonardo M (5)     119

## Wandsworth Preparatory School, London

| | |
|---|---|
| Eli Lees (6) | 120 |
| Felix Mullineux (5) | 121 |
| Salvador Ernst (6) | 122 |
| Riley Yule (6) | 123 |
| Maximilian Turner (5) | 124 |
| Iseoluwa Apollon (5) | 125 |
| Balazs Simon (7) | 126 |

## Warren Road Primary School, Orpington

| | |
|---|---|
| Hayley Wood (5) | 127 |

## Whitehorse Manor Junior School, Thornton Heath

| | |
|---|---|
| Brook Spiby Pickering (7) | 128 |
| Edison Spiby Pickering (5) | 129 |

# The Poems

# Cockapoos

**C** ute as a baby

**O** verly fluffy like a lamb

**C** razy as a monkey - jumpy as can be

**K** een to smell every little crumb!

**A** gile and energetic, running from here to there

**P** layful puppy with paws as soft as silk

**O** bedient like me at school!

**O** ut of this world - my pet Ramsey!

## Phoebe Cullimore (7)

Bramford CE (VC) Primary School, Bramford

1

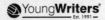 
# White Rhinos

**W** hite rhinos are big
**H** ungry and grumpy
**I** n Africa
**T** wo horns
**E** yes are tiny

**R** hinos are strong
**H** orns are sharp
**I** have a little tail
**N** ow almost extinct
**O** nly one left.

## Isobelle Reeve (5)

Bramford CE (VC) Primary School, Bramford

# Crocodiles

**C** hompy

**R** aised

**O** verly sharp teeth

**C** arnivore

**O** pen their mouths wide

**D** eep water swimmers

**I** live in the Everglades in Florida

**L** ove to eat meat

**E** xtremely sharp teeth.

## Daisy-Mae Reeve (7)

Bramford CE (VC) Primary School, Bramford

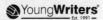

# Cheetah

**C** heetahs are the fastest animals in the world

**H** unts for meat

**E** njoys playing in the grass

**E** very cheetah is dangerous

**T** hey have spots on their bodies

**A** very fast cat

**H** ave sharp claws.

**Pippa Lyon (6)**

Bramford CE (VC) Primary School, Bramford

# Rabbit

**R** abbits dig holes

**A** rabbit poos in our garden

**B** ouncing is what they like to do

**B** ig fluffy ears

**I** n summer, rabbits seek the comfort of their burrows

**T** hey have twitchy noses.

## Oscar Pemberton (6)

Bramford CE (VC) Primary School, Bramford

# Phoenix Are Great!

**P** eaceful, calm and still
**H** onest, gentle and loyal
**O** riginal, they do their own thing!
**E** xciting they are!
**N** ew bodies come from the ashes
**I** nteresting they all are!
**X** -ray insight into new beginnings.

## Charlotte Partridge (7)
Charford First School, Charford

# Giraffe

**G** iraffes are strong and ginormous with skinny legs like sticks

**I** ntelligent animal having fun in the hot blazing sun

**R** ising up to feed on the juicy luscious leaves

**A** iming for the beautiful blue sky with their young

**F** riendly giraffes shading under the big green bushy trees

**F** antastic and magnificent to watch them feed with their long necks like a ladder

**E** normous, energetic and exotic - the giraffe is loved by all!

## Anniyah Hussain (6)

Eden Park Primary School Academy, Brixham

# Rabbit

**R** abbits running, racing round, rummaging for some tasty grass

**A** rabbit's tail is as white as snow and fluffy like a dandelion

**B** aby rabbits are called a kit. So cute and as fluffy as candyfloss

**B** ouncing bunnies acrobatically running as fast as they can

**I** n and out of their warrens, safe and snuggly in their homes

**T** urning their ears amazingly 180 degrees to listen out for their predators.

## Isla Jones (7)
Eden Park Primary School Academy, Brixham

# Monkey

M anic monkeys climbing up the trees

O range orangutans live on little islands at the zoo

N ot many monkeys have moustaches, but little Emperor tamarins do

K ing of the jungle, the gorilla beats his fists on his chest like a drum

E ye spy with my little eye, a smelly baboon and his pink bum

Y ellow flowers the cheeky chimpanzee sniffed. *Achoo! Achoo!*

## Joshua Fox (7)

Eden Park Primary School Academy, Brixham

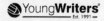
# Elephant

**E** smae the enormous elephant

**L** oves swinging her stick-like tail

**E** ars that flap when she stomps down the trees

**P** lants, herbs and leaves is all that Esmae needs

**H** er long trunk she uses to drink water

**A** nd cools herself down in the sun

**N** ever forgetting is the elephant's way

**T** aking food home for the herd for the day.

## Katie Gill (7)

Eden Park Primary School Academy, Brixham

# Caterpillar

**C** an you see me?
**A** little cute creature
**T** ons of tiny toes
**E** ating lots of leaves
**R** aindrops for drinking
**P** atiently waiting to perform
**I** am getting ready to transform
**L** ittle by little I spin my silk
**L** ayered like an onion
**A** mazing like magic
**R** eady! I am now a butterfly!

## Sonny Laywood (5)
Eden Park Primary School Academy, Brixham

# Slow Worm

**S** hiny smooth bodies
**L** ooks like a snake
**O** ccasionally we eat small insects
**W** e eat up to 20 slugs per day

**W** oodland areas are where we love to live
**O** ctober to March we hide away to stay
warm and safe
**R** ocks are where we like to hide
**M** ales are mostly grey with blue spots.

## Riley Perrott (7)

Eden Park Primary School Academy, Brixham

12

# Elephant

**E** at plants high up in trees
**L** eaves are very good for them
**E** normous ears flapping around
**P** lease don't get too close
**H** eavy feet stomping around
**A** nd sharp, strong tusks
**N** ever get too close
**T** usks, trunk and long swishy tail.

## Annabella Tolly (6)

Eden Park Primary School Academy, Brixham

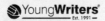
# Koalas

**K** oalas kissing kids, how nice that would be to see

**O** h, to sleep all day in a tree, how lazy they must be

**A** ll fuzzy like bees

**L** ove munching leaves from trees

**A** s they carry their joey on their back

**S** neakily hiding from a predator's attack.

## Rosie Lewis (6)
Eden Park Primary School Academy, Brixham

# Sea Otter

S wimming on their backs
E ating tasty urchins
A nd crabs that go pinch

O n their backs they sleep holding hands
T rying not to float away
T ruly cute and cuddly
E xtremely fluffy like a cat
R eminding me of Canada.

## Isaac Wilson (6)

Eden Park Primary School Academy, Brixham

# Puffin

**P** uffins are black and white with bright orange legs

**U** nder the water they swim to catch their dinner

**F** ish is their favourite food

**F** lying high in the sky

**I** celand is where they like to lay their eggs

**N** icknamed 'Penguin of the North'.

## Lilly Collins-Dryer (6)

Eden Park Primary School Academy, Brixham

# Cheetah!

**C** reeping cautiously through the grass
**H** unting carefully for its prey
**E** xtremely quiet
**E** xceptionally fast, fierce and ferocious
**T** eeth that are sharp, strong and shiny
**A** lert and always on the look out
**H** ungry for its next meal.

## Robyn Woodland (6)

Eden Park Primary School Academy, Brixham

# Tigers

**T** errifying tigers are threatening, massive wild cats

**I** nto the night they go hunting for antelope and wild pigs

**G** iant animals that are great swimmers

**E** ven wild cats have super stripes and are hairy

**R** oar as loud as a lion, tigers are scary!

## Barney Roberts (6)

Eden Park Primary School Academy, Brixham

# Giraffe

**G** iants that gobble gracefully

**I** ts neck is as long as a ladder

**R** eaches high to eat leaves

**A** s for sleep, they don't get much

**F** ull of power - but shy

**F** our long legs they have

**E** nough to make them run fast.

## Max Parker (5)

Eden Park Primary School Academy, Brixham

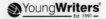
# Scary Snakes

**S** ome are harmless and some are not
**N** eedle-shaped fangs are sharp and pointy
**A** lmost as long as humans
**K** ill their prey by squeezing them
**E** nd of their tongue senses their food
**S** tripes and diamonds can be seen on them.

## Luca Holmes (6)
Eden Park Primary School Academy, Brixham

# Narwhal Life

**N** autical marine mammal

**A** quatic habitat

**R** aging battles with other males

**W** hale with a horn, like a mystical creature

**H** orned unicorn of the sea

**A** rctic wanderers

**L** ives in a pod.

## Daisy Brown (7)

Eden Park Primary School Academy, Brixham

# Puppy

**P** layful puppy Poppy loves playing with her ball

**U** nder the table she goes and finds lots of toys

**P** aws with sharp claws

**P** oppy playing in the snow

**Y** oung Poppy is tired - *snore, snore, snore.*

## Felicity Brounger (7)
Eden Park Primary School Academy, Brixham

# Leopard

**L** ovely leopard looking for food

**E** ating meat

**O** ver the grass it leaps

**P** reying for food

**A** nd watching the trees move

**R** oaring from the distance

**D** ancing through the grass.

## Lily Goodburn (6)

Eden Park Primary School Academy, Brixham

# Tiger

**T** iptoeing on his big soft paws
**I** nside savannah's wildest lawns
**G** reat Bengal tiger hunts for prey
**E** lephants, buffalos, langurs the grey
**R** un for their lives to escape in the bay.

## William Goodinson (6)
Eden Park Primary School Academy, Brixham

# We Went To See A Tiger

**T** oday we went to see a tiger

**I** t had big claws

**G** *rrr*, it said as it looked at us

**E** veryone stared at the tiger and the tiger stared back

**R** oman thought that it was very scary!

## Roman Mooney (5)

Eden Park Primary School Academy, Brixham

# Tigers

**T** eatime is meat time
**I** n the jungle tigers jump on their prey
**G** reen long grass is where tigers hide
**E** very tiny tiger cub is born blind
**R** unning fast is a tiger's superpower.

## Reuben Dodgson (6)
Eden Park Primary School Academy, Brixham

# Happy Hippo

**H** appy hungry hippo
**I** s a very happy chappie
**P** lanning the day after dreaming away
**P** laying away in the mudbank today
**O** nly a happy hungry hippo takes naps in-between play.

## Seren Morgans (6)

Eden Park Primary School Academy, Brixham

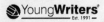
# Monkey

**M** ischievous Mike
**O** nly likes to
**N** ibble on nuts, whilst he
**K** eeps on playing catch, as he is
**E** nergetic and always on the go
**Y** ou will laugh at his crazy ways.

## Lydia Temple (7)
Eden Park Primary School Academy, Brixham

# Zebra

**Z** ebras are stripy
**E** xcellent eyesight and smell
**B** elieve it, they sleep standing up
**R** eally fast at running away from lions
**A** ll zebras have their own stripe pattern.

## Esme Greatbatch (6)

Eden Park Primary School Academy, Brixham

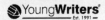

# Meggie

**M** y nannie's dog is black
**E** ating her food while
**G** rowling at cats, she is fast
**G** ardening with me
**I** n the sunshine and I
**E** njoy my time with Meggie.

## Harry Powder

Eden Park Primary School Academy, Brixham

# Hairy Horse

**H** airy horse feels soft
**O** utside eating yummy green grass
**R** unning as fast as it can
**S** unbathing in a buttercup field
**E** yes are big and round.

## Dulcie Hall-Green (5)

Eden Park Primary School Academy, Brixham

# Sloths

S low and
L azy Sally the sloth is
O nly moving for
T hose delicious leaves
H anging around all day
S leeping the time away.

## Nikita Kimble (7)
Eden Park Primary School Academy, Brixham

# Bunny

**B** ouncing around the place

**U** p and down

**N** ice as a puppy

**N** eeds soft, snuggly shelter

**Y** ou might not find him when he's hiding.

## India Moore (7)

Eden Park Primary School Academy, Brixham

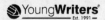

# Shark

**S** ilently swimming in the sea
**H** uge hunters, looking for their prey
**A** ttack!
**R** uling the reef
**K** ing of all the fish.

## Mahlia Dobbs (7)
Eden Park Primary School Academy, Brixham

# The Fabulous Cat

**C** harlie was a ginger and white cat!

**A** nd he was rather fat!

**T** ricky and quick, he liked to lick himself on a black and white mat!

## Lily-May Stevens (7)

Eden Park Primary School Academy, Brixham

# Dog

**D** ingo the dinky dog dug a deep hole
**O** ften he would bury his bone
**G** *rowl*, grunted Dingo as grumpy as a grandad.

## Vinny Ingham (7)
Eden Park Primary School Academy, Brixham

# Fish

**F** riendly fish slapping those fins
**I** like to watch them
**S** wim like a fish
**H** appily in the water.

## Jayden Crump (7)
Eden Park Primary School Academy, Brixham

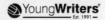
# Dogs

**D** irty dogs dive into ditches
**O** ne poo a day
**G** oing for walks
**S** melly like a soggy sock.

## Mollie Turnbull (7)

Eden Park Primary School Academy, Brixham

# Dogs

**D** igging holes for fun
**O** ld bones to eat
**G** reen grass to run in
**S** leeps by my side.

## Gabriel Watts (6)

Eden Park Primary School Academy, Brixham

# Spotty Cheetahs

C heetahs live in Asia and Africa
H unting for food they want
E ating juicy gazelles
E very cheetah has different spots
T he cheetah is different to other cats
A t great speed they run
H ave a tail to help them balance when
they run
S peed kings they are.

## Eliza Smith (6)

Eldon Grove Academy, Hartlepool

# Intelligent Elephants

**E** xcellent hearing

**L** ong grey trunks

**E** lephants are normally boys

**P** laytime in the bath

**H** eavy babies

**A** frican elephants have bigger ears than Asian

**N** oses are like a trumpet

**T** usks are sharp

**S** mart big elephants.

## Angelica Solomon (7)

Eldon Grove Academy, Hartlepool

# Butterfly

**B** utterflies eat the flowers
**U** tterly pretty
**T** hey live in South America
**T** hey can fly by flapping their wings
**E** ggs turn into caterpillars
**R** eally colourful
**F** lutter all around
**L** ovely butterfly
**Y** ummy leaves.

## Pixie Liddle (7)
Eldon Grove Academy, Hartlepool

# Butterfly

**B** utterflies can fly

**U** p they go

**T** hey have yellow skin

**T** hey try to fly

**E** yes look at other butterflies

**R** ainbow coloured

**F** loating up they go

**L** ive in South America

**Y** ellow patterns everywhere.

## Rory Betts (6)

Eldon Grove Academy, Hartlepool

# Rainbow Narwhal

**N** ot fluffy at all
**A** s soon as they're in water they're wet
**R** are species
**W** ater blows out of its blowhole
**H** ave a beautiful horn
**A** rctic waters are their home
**L** ovely and cute animals.

## Ailsa Grey (7)
Eldon Grove Academy, Hartlepool

# Wings

**P** retty to look at

**A** mazing bird

**R** ainforests they live in

**A** mazing speed in flight

**K** eep clinging onto twigs

**E** very day they fly

**E** very bird is special

**T** hey are lovely.

## Jemima Catherine Horsley (7)

Eldon Grove Academy, Hartlepool

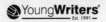

# Komodo Dragon

**K** omodos like to eat deer
**O** nly don't like others
**M** ost spit venom
**O** ne very dangerous animal
**D** on't go near. Nooo!
**O** ver the sandy places they stroll.

## Luke McManus
Eldon Grove Academy, Hartlepool

# Pet Tortoise

**T** ickly claws

**O** nly stay on land

**R** eally slow

**T** ortoises eat vegetables

**O** nly drink water

**I** ntelligent

**S** lowly walk

**E** yes that are blue.

## Esme Kate Pullen (7)

Eldon Grove Academy, Hartlepool

# Sloth

**S** loths are very slow
**L** azy sloths hang in the trees all day
**O** nly go to the toilet once a week
**T** hey hang upside down in a tree
**H** ave two or three claws.

## Ella Rose Hodgson (7)

Eldon Grove Academy, Hartlepool

# Sloth

**S** tay in trees

**L** azily hanging on the branch

**O** nly go to the toilet once a week

**T** hey live in tropical rainforests

**H** as sharp claws to stay on the branch.

## Phoebe Alice Sabourin (7)

Eldon Grove Academy, Hartlepool

# Scary Lions

**L** ions do a scary roar!
**I** nteresting creatures living in the wild
**O** h wait. One is looking at me
**N** ooo! Just be careful
**S** neaky creatures they are.

## Danielle Mitchell (7)
Eldon Grove Academy, Hartlepool

# Cute Rabbits

**R** abbits run for their food
**A** fter the food they go to bed
**B** aby bunnies are born
**B** ig fluffy ears
**I** t has soft fur
**T** oo cute.

## Elizabeth Edith Grainger (7)

Eldon Grove Academy, Hartlepool

# Sloths

S loths are cute
L ovely and cuddly
O n the trees all of the time
T hey go to the toilet only once a week
H ang on branches.

## Idha Hildreth (6)

Eldon Grove Academy, Hartlepool

# Pet Cats

**C** ats have loads of liver and snacks
**A** fter their food they can jump very high
**T** hey live in your house
**S** ome pet cats are friendly.

## Phoebe Harrison (7)

Eldon Grove Academy, Hartlepool

# Bears

**B** ears eat yummy meat
**E** xtremely slow
**A** lways hunt
**R** *oarrrr!* Let me taste you!
**S** aw you. Time to eat you!

## Jack Marsey (7)
Eldon Grove Academy, Hartlepool

# Sloth

**S** low and sleepy
**L** ong claws
**O** ne is looking at me
**T** rees are their home
**H** ot countries are better for them.

## Harley Sweeting (7)
Eldon Grove Academy, Hartlepool

# Fish

**F** ish find something to eat
**I** n the water they eat all day
**S** wimming around in the water
**H** iding behind lots of rocks.

## Alex Hung (7)

Eldon Grove Academy, Hartlepool

# Lion

**L** ong, furry and swishy tail
**I** n Africa they can be found
**O** h no, they're dangerous!
**N** ooo, I got eaten!

## Adelaide Merrifield-Burke (7)
Eldon Grove Academy, Hartlepool

# Deadly Cats

**C** uddly and warm
**A** dorable
**T** ea is a mouse for him
**S** ilent but deadly.

## Brodie Campbell (7)
Eldon Grove Academy, Hartlepool

# Dogs

**D** ogs are cute
**O** wners look after them
**G** rowl loudly
**S** pecial pets.

## Jade Storey (7)

Eldon Grove Academy, Hartlepool

# Elephant

**E** lephants are excellent
**L** ong trunks for picking up food
**E** normous but clumsy
**P** retty good shooting out sparkling water
**H** andy for helping you
**A** ctually gigantic
**N** aughty baby elephants don't follow their mums
**T** runks are used for smelling, they are my favourite.

## Lyla Wisbey (7)
Enborne CE Primary School, Enborne

# Dippy Dinosaurs

**D** iplodocus moves on four legs
**I** rritator is a carnivore
**N** edoceratops has two horns
**O** viraptor steals eggs
**S** tegosaurus has spikes on his back
**A** nchisaurus eats plants
**U** tahraptor moves on two legs
**R** ugops is a scavenger
**S** o many different dinosaurs.

## Harry Pearce (6)
Enborne CE Primary School, Enborne

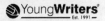
# I Love Unicorns

**U** nicorns are magical creatures
**N** ight-time is when I dream about them
**I** love unicorns
**C** ute unicorns are lovely
**O** nly unicorns can do magic
**R** unning and jumping all day
**N** ice unicorns are kind
**S** imply the best.

## Nina Powell (6)
Enborne CE Primary School, Enborne

# Magical Sparkling Unicorn

**U** nique, beautiful and magical

**N** o one thinks they are real

**I** believe in unicorns

**C** rystals hang from their mane

**O** ver the rainbow they fly

**R** unning very swiftly

**N** ever be unkind or mean.

## Gracie Keel (6)
Enborne CE Primary School, Enborne

# Koala

**K** oalas are cuddly and sweet
**O** f all the plants they like to eat
**A** re the leaves of the eucalyptus tree
**L** ush and green but not very nutritious
**A** lways to them are particularly delicious.

## Harvey Burton (7)
Enborne CE Primary School, Enborne

# Mouse

**M** ice are very small and fast
**O** n the hunt for cheese and snacks
**U** nder floors and hiding in cracks
**S** cared of cats in your house
**E** lephants are scared of that tiny mouse.

## Oliver Withers (8)

Enborne CE Primary School, Enborne

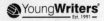

# Monkey

**M** arvellous cheeky monkeys
**O** n a treetop
**N** ever get too close
**K** eep your hat on
**E** nd the hat stealing, monkey
**Y** ou'll feel bad if you don't.

## Tamilore Ganiyu (7)
Enborne CE Primary School, Enborne

# Sheep

**S** heep are woolly

**H** appy sheep baa

**E** very day sheep eat grass

**E** wes are female sheep

**P** lease look after sheep.

## Georgina Murray (5)
Enborne CE Primary School, Enborne

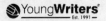

# Echidna

**E** gg laying
**C** ute
**H** airy creature
**I** n Australia
**D** igs a lot
**N** o teeth
**A** nt eating.

## Freddie Ashbrook (8)
Enborne CE Primary School, Enborne

# Dog

**D** on't bite me little doggy
**O** ne year and Jack went pony riding
**G** race went to the shop.

## Ethan Hawkett (6)
Enborne CE Primary School, Enborne

# Rabbit

**R** uns for carrots every time
**A** round my garden all the time
**B** ig nails on my rabbit claws
**B** ouncing around my garden
**I** love my rabbit
**T** ails like a ball of fluff.

## Melek Ozsevgec (6)
Hindhayes Infant School, Street

# Horse

H orses like to eat hay

O ften eat grass

R uns in a field

S ome horses run around the paddock

E very horse has a colourful mane.

## Bo Birkett (6)

Hindhayes Infant School, Street

# Dogs

**D** ogs have collars
**O** range dogs are rare
**G** ood dogs get treats
**S** ome dogs protect owners.

## Archie Duffy (6)
Hindhayes Infant School, Street

# Fish

F ish need clean water
I love fish of orange
S parkly scales
H ave dirty tanks.

## Tamzin Austwick (5)

Hindhayes Infant School, Street

# Dogs

**D** ogs like dog food
**O** ften chats
**G** ets a ball and gives it to his owner.

## Emily Buxton (6)

Hindhayes Infant School, Street

# Paper

**D** ogs run so fast
**O** ver a log
**G** ot me a paper towel.

## Leo Carombayenin (5)

Hindhayes Infant School, Street

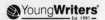

# Dogs

D ogs run fast
O wners love them
G et a dog.

## Jack Molland (6)

Hindhayes Infant School, Street

# Meerkat

**M** eerkats are nice

**E** xcellent diggers

**E** ating insects and creepy-crawlies

**R** unning around having fun

**K** eeping watch for predators

**A** wesome animals

**T** ogether they survive.

## Ava Sinclair (6)

Holy Cross & All Saints RC Primary School, Eccles

# Elephant

**E** lephants eat mud and hay
**L** arge trunk
**E** lephants have tusks
**P** lay squirting water
**H** erd the elephants
**A** nd has a trunk
**N** oisy elephants
**T** errific elephants.

## Dillon Dwyer (6)

Holy Cross & All Saints RC Primary School, Eccles

# Jaguars

**J** aguars
**A** n incredible animal
**G** reat runner
**U** nusual animal
**A** s they catch their prey they eat it
**R** are animal
**S** neakers.

## Felix Krzykwa (6)
Holy Cross & All Saints RC Primary School, Eccles

# Elephant

**E** lephant

**L** ong trunk

**E** normous ears

**P** rotect their young

**H** erd

**A** re very big

**N** oisy trumpet

**T** usks.

## Kevin Mathew (6), William Vennard (5) & Daniel Jackson (6)

Holy Cross & All Saints RC Primary School, Eccles

# Cheetah

**C** atching prey

**H** unt for food

**E** at meat

**E** at animals

**T** ough and never gives up

**A** large cat

**H** ave survived.

## Basit Dauda (6)

Holy Cross & All Saints RC Primary School, Eccles

# Cheetah

**C** laws are sharp

**H** e runs very fast

**E** ats meat

**E** nergetic

**T** hey have spots

**A** thletic

**H** ide in the bush.

## Evelyn Nel (5)

Holy Cross & All Saints RC Primary School, Eccles

# Monkey

**M** onkeys can climb trees

**O** n the branches

**N** aughty monkeys

**K** eep on swinging

**E** ats bananas

**Y** es they are running.

## Finley Winter (6)

Holy Cross & All Saints RC Primary School, Eccles

# Tiger

**T** hey like to eat meat
**I** n the jungle
**G** reat at catching their prey
**E** ating predators
**R** un fast.

## Ethan Milton (6)

Holy Cross & All Saints RC Primary School, Eccles

# Bats

**B** ats have good hearing
**A** t night they come to eat food
**T** hey hang upside down
**S** o happy on the trees.

## Harry McGill (6)

Holy Cross & All Saints RC Primary School, Eccles

# Lion

**L** ives in Africa and India
**I** mpressive mane
**O** ne awesome creature
**N** estling in the grass.

## Joshua Hallworth (6)
Holy Cross & All Saints RC Primary School, Eccles

# Zebra

**Z** ebras
**E** at grass
**B** lack and white stripes
**R** uns fast
**A** brave animal.

## Joshua Pollock (6) & Sam
Holy Cross & All Saints RC Primary School, Eccles

# Bats

**B** ats are black
**A** t night
**T** hey hang upside down
**S** leep in the day.

## Oscar Pennington (6)

Holy Cross & All Saints RC Primary School, Eccles

# Rhinoceros

**R** eally big and strong
**H** andsome with spiky horns
**I** s a little chubby
**N** ot a bit grubby
**O** ne or two horns that will hurt you
**C** ome look and see, I will show you
**E** asily as big as a house
**R** ight, let's run
**O** ver the sun
**S** miling, we are safe from the rhinoceros.

## Marcus Pope-Brannon (7)

Kessingland CE Primary Academy, Kessingland

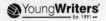

# Spiders

**S** pins a web to catch flies
**P** oisons their prey with venom
**I** t takes 60 minutes to spin a web
**D** on't live in the cold places like the
Antarctic
**E** ight legs to scurry around
**R** un upside down on the ceiling and glass
**S** piders are arachnids.

## Henry Daws (7)
Kessingland CE Primary Academy, Kessingland

90

# Giraffe

**G** rowing taller every day
**I** n the trees eating leaves
**R** aising their necks high
**A** nd nearly reaching the sky
**F** unny long legs
**F** ull of spots
**E** veryone loves a giraffe.

## Fred Capps-Smith (6)

Kessingland CE Primary Academy, Kessingland

# All About A Tiger

**T** heir babies are called cubs
**I** n Asia they sleep in forests
**G** oes hunting for meat
**E** very tiger has stripes
**R** *oar!*

## Niamh Weatherington (6)
Kessingland CE Primary Academy, Kessingland

# You Get To Know The Hippo!

H ippos are heavy

I n Africa they live

P laying is what they do

P lants are what they eat

O xygen is what they breathe.

## Buddy Byron-Weatherill (6)

Kessingland CE Primary Academy, Kessingland

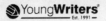
# My Pet Dotty

**C** ute and cuddly
**A** lways hungry
**T** otally awesome.

## Imogen Loud (7)
Kessingland CE Primary Academy, Kessingland

# Anglerfish

**A** ngry looking

**N** ot smiling

**G** oes down deep

**L** ights up bright

**E** ats his prey

**R** eally sharp teeth

**F** rightening fish

**I** n the dark

**S** wims sneakily

**H** ungry all the time.

## Alfie Smith (6)

Magna Carta Primary Academy, Stansted Mountfitchet

# Rabbit

**R** elaxed and happy, you purr like a cat on a lap

**A** mazing long ears can turn 180 degrees

**B** inkying with joy, you hop, twist and kick

**B** urrowing in the ground, you make a home where you are as snug as a bug in a rug

**I** nto the vegetable patch you sneak as quietly as a mouse to steal some carrots to eat

**T** iny kittens enter the world with their eyes shut tight like people asleep.

## Roseanna Sloper (7)

Old Buckenham Hall School, Ipswich

# Armadillo

**A** rmoured plates that make them indestructible

**R** oll up into a ball to hide from predators

**M** ost live in North and South America

**A** nts are their favourite food

**D** igging down in the dirty ground

**I** nflatable stomachs let them float on water

**L** ittle legs make them

**L** ow to the ground

**O** h to be an armadillo.

## Rufus Wells (7)

Old Buckenham Hall School, Ipswich

# The Cheetah

**C** is for coalition, which is the group that males live in

**H** is for has spots all over its body

**E** is for eating meat for its lunch

**E** is for enjoying playing in the grass

**T** is for tigers we are not!

**A** is for Africa where we live

**H** is for hunters that hunt us

**S** is for sad, which is how that makes me feel.

## Samuel Gosling (7)

Old Buckenham Hall School, Ipswich

# Minotaur

**M** assive horns on his furry head

**I** ntense, fiery eyes burning like bonfires, staring at your

**N** aughty children

**O** bviously made up - a Greek myth

**T** errorising children at midnight as he chases them

**A** round the labyrinth

**U** tterly vicious and mean

**R** eally revolting and rare.

## Thomas Gillman (7)

Old Buckenham Hall School, Ipswich

# Chicken

**C** ockerels are loud and annoying
**H** ens lay little hatching eggs
**I** ncubating 21 days for fluffy chicks
**C** razy foxes cannot have them for dinner
**K** ennels give them a safe home
**E** ggs are super yummy
**N** ow I will have my dippy egg.

## Sophie Keaney (7)
Old Buckenham Hall School, Ipswich

# My Labrador Called Tumi

**D** azzling, shiny golden coat shimmering like a star

**O** ften she plays in the garden with me catching balls

**G** rowls like thunder when she sees dogs and cats she doesn't like

**S** uper fast like a lightning bolt, she runs after me on my bike.

## Lauren Hewitt (7)
Old Buckenham Hall School, Ipswich

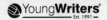

# King Of The Carnivores

**S** avage saber-tooth
**M** ost powerful cat of all
**I** ncredibly fierce predator
**L** ong, sharp front teeth
**O** ld as a tough mammoth
**D** eadly canines
**O** utrageously strong
**N** eck full of muscle.

## Giles Roberts (6)

Old Buckenham Hall School, Ipswich

# Bees

**B** uzzing bees that have a beautiful queen bee

**E** ating their sticky yellow honey just like us

**E** ach worker collects sticky pollen from flowers

**S** tinging with their sharp bottoms only if they are scared.

## Charlotte Warner (7)
Old Buckenham Hall School, Ipswich

# Cheetah

**C** lever predator
**H** as amazing eyesight
**E** ats gazelles and wildebeest
**E** xcellent tree climbers
**T** all grass helps them hide
**A** re super speedy
**H** as lots of spots.

## Flora Surguy (5)
Old Buckenham Hall School, Ipswich

# Goldfish

**G** ulping gills

**O** range gold skin

**L** azing around

**D** ancing for food

**F** lipping his fins

**I** nk coloured plants

**S** tones to suck on

**H** ome safe and cosy.

## Amelia Mason-Sinclair (7)

Old Buckenham Hall School, Ipswich

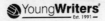
# Cheetah

**C** lever camouflage
**H** unts during the day
**E** xcellent eyesight
**E** legant looking
**T** hreatened species
**A** frica's big cat
**H** unts at over 60mph.

## Daisy Templer (6)
Old Buckenham Hall School, Ipswich

# Bunny's Adventure

**B** ouncing up and down
**U** nbelievably adorable
**N** ibbling carrots all day long
**N** aughty games of hide-and-seek
**Y** ummy lettuce from the garden.

## Rosie Clark (7)
Old Buckenham Hall School, Ipswich

# Chimps

**C** heeky chimp
**H** igh in the trees
**I** mp of the forest
**M** onkey and apes
**P** laying catch with the bananas.

## Rory Ramsay (6)

Old Buckenham Hall School, Ipswich

# Lamb

**L** ively, lovely lamby
**A** dorable, amazing lamby
**M** ini sheep in massive meadows
**B** ounding, bouncing, bleating.

## Nixon Johnson (7)
Old Buckenham Hall School, Ipswich

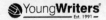

# Gorilla

**G** igantic

**O** mnivore

**R** are

**I** ntelligent

**L** azy

**L** oud

**A** frican.

## Llywelyn Griffiths (6)

Old Buckenham Hall School, Ipswich

# British Blue

**B** lue grey coat
**R** otating to sit down
**I** ndependent
**T** ame and friendly
**I** ntelligent
**S** oft and snuggly
**H** appy, smiley face

**B** all of fluff
**L** icking and washing
**U** sually asleep
**E** yes are copper.

## Arthur Price (6)
St John's Priory School, Banbury

# Crocodile

**C** laws so sharp
**R** iver so blue
**O** live-green scales
**C** atching prey
**O** pen jaws wide
**D** iving deep, deep down
**I** n the mud
**L** ying on their tummy
**E** yes so yellow.

## Arthur Price (6)
St John's Priory School, Banbury

# Alien

**A** rms on her long legs

**L** egs that are bouncy and wobbly when
she runs slow

**I** s funny and happy, then runs fast

**E** yes that glow in the night

**N** ose is gooey and soft.

## Atia D
St John's Priory School, Banbury

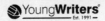 

# Alien

**A** big friendly alien
**L** ong silky webs from his hands
**I** s a monster flying from outer space
**E** yes are blue and glowing
**N** o mouth, no noise.

## Jayden T (6)
St John's Priory School, Banbury

# Alien

**A** rms on the side of his body
**L** egs are bumpy and short
**I** s fast and wobbly
**E** ars are dangly and funny
**N** ew alien is very funny.

## Charlotte A (6)

St John's Priory School, Banbury

# Alien

**A** stink from his stomach
**L** ong legs and neck
**I** s very crazy and friendly
**E** ars on springs to help him hear
**N** oisy and snotty.

## Ash L
St John's Priory School, Banbury

# Alien

**A** rms with claws

**L** ove heart body

**I** s very noisy and loud

**E** yes spring out of the Mars alien

**N** osy alien, jumping about.

## Beatrix M (6)

St John's Priory School, Banbury

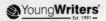

# Alien

**A** big naughty alien
**L** ong springy neck
**I** s very silly and naughty
**E** yes are everywhere
**N** ot very smart and clever.

## Xavier R
St John's Priory School, Banbury

# Alien

**A** rms on his tummy

**L** ong, slimy green legs

**I** s very funny and crazy

**E** yes are different colours

**N** ice friend.

## Leonardo M (5)
St John's Priory School, Banbury

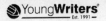

# Snake

**S** ly
**N** oisy with a rattling tail
**A** mazing fangs
**K** illing animals
**E** xcellent scales.

## Eli Lees (6)
Wandsworth Preparatory School, London

# Shark

**S** harp teeth
**H** ard fin
**A** lways hunting
**R** eally strong body
**K** ing of the ocean.

## Felix Mullineux (5)

Wandsworth Preparatory School, London

# Shark

**S** harp teeth
**H** ungry
**A** ngry shark
**R** ushing through the sea
**K** iller animal.

## Salvador Ernst (6)
Wandsworth Preparatory School, London

# Fish

**F** ins
**I** t swims in the water
**S** wimming fish
**H** unting for food.

## Riley Yule (6)

Wandsworth Preparatory School, London

# Dogs

**D** igging dogs
**O** n a lead
**G** rubby legs and paws
**S** melly body.

## Maximilian Turner (5)

Wandsworth Preparatory School, London

# Pony

**P** retty pony
**O** n the grass
**N** oisy hooves
**Y** ou can ride it.

## Iseoluwa Apollon (5)

Wandsworth Preparatory School, London

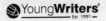

# Fish

**F** ins
**I** n the sea
**S** wim
**H** ungry.

## Balazs Simon (7)

Wandsworth Preparatory School, London

# A Zebra

**Z** ebras are related to horses and donkeys
**E** ats green grass
**B** lack and white stripes
**R** uns in herds
**A** frican plains.

## Hayley Wood (5)

Warren Road Primary School, Orpington

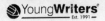

# The Emperors!

**P** enguins have really bad tempers!

**E** mperor penguins go *flip-flop* on their flippers

**N** o, you don't want to fight with a penguin, they really go for it!

**G** orgeous smooth feathers

**U** nderwater swimming for penguins is really elegant and beautiful

**I** ndoors for penguins - no, no no! Outdoors in the wild - yes, yes, yes!

**N** ot the Arctic, penguins live in Antarctica.

## Brook Spiby Pickering (7)
Whitehorse Manor Junior School, Thornton Heath

# King Hippo

**H** e is happy in the mud
**I** ncredible hippos
**P** eep out of the water
**P** ee in the water too!
**O** pen jaws show big teeth
**P** urplish when wet, but grey
**O** r pink on their ears
**T** empers of hippos are bad!
**A** nd they hold their breath
**M** iles they walk to find food
**U** nderwater walking
**S** kin covered in scars.

## Edison Spiby Pickering (5)
Whitehorse Manor Junior School, Thornton Heath

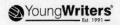 **Young Writers** Est. 1991

# Young Writers Information

We hope you have enjoyed reading this book – and that you will continue to in the coming years.

If you're a young writer who enjoys reading and creative writing, or the parent of an enthusiastic poet or story writer, do visit our website **www.youngwriters.co.uk**. Here you will find free competitions, workshops and games, as well as recommended reads, a poetry glossary and our blog. There's lots to keep budding writers motivated to write!

If you would like to order further copies of this book, or any of our other titles, then please give us a call or order via your online account.

Young Writers
Remus House
Coltsfoot Drive
Peterborough
PE2 9BF
(01733) 890066
**info@youngwriters.co.uk**

Join in the conversation!
Tips, news, giveaways and much more!

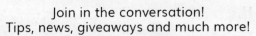

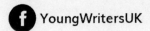 YoungWritersUK

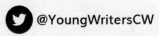 @YoungWritersCW